# RUDYARD [KIPLI]NG'S

# HOW THE CAMEL GOT HIS HUMP

## THE GRAPHIC NOVEL

### Simonson & Rodriguez

# TO OUR READERS

The animal world has long been a place of intrigue. Countless mysteries surround its magnificent creatures. For years, humankind has wondered how animals came to look and act the way they do.

Finally, the questions have been answered. Famed author and worldwide explorer Rudyard Kipling has traveled the globe, searching for the greatest of beasts. He's witnessed and recorded animal behaviors unlike anything seen before. And now he is sharing his findings with the world.

Let Kipling be your guide as you journey into jungles, grasslands, and deserts. Use his invaluable research to unravel the mysteries yourself. It is an exciting time for animal lovers. Thanks to Kipling, we can all be part of it.

Sincerely,
The Editors

# HOW THE CAMEL GOT HIS HUMP

RUDYARD KIPLING

# RESEARCH

**SPECIMEN:**
**FLAT-BACKED CAMEL** (Fig. A)

**SOCIAL BEHAVIOR:** 'Scruciatingly idle
**DIET:** Milkweed, tamarisks, and prickles (Fig. B)
**HABITAT:** Howling Desert (Fig. C)
**FELLOW DESERT DWELLER:** Djinn (Fig. D)
**NEARBY ANIMALS:** Dog (Fig. E);
Oxen (Fig. F); and Horse (Fig. G)

**B**

Dumb
grin

**A**

Smooth,
flat back

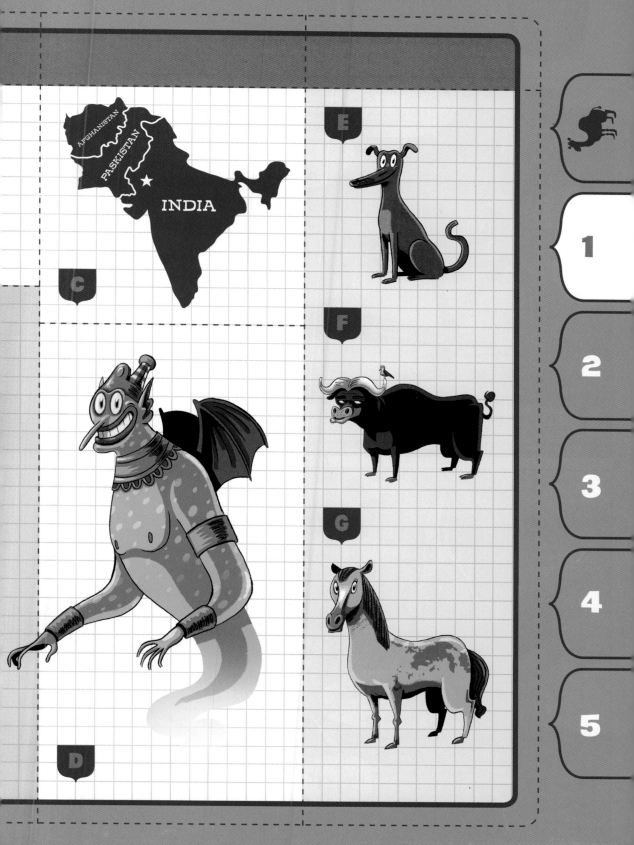

He is called a *Camel!* A lazy, *bad-tempered* beast!

He thinks he is *too good* to work like the *rest* of us!

Go *find him*, Horse! Tell that *lazy* Camel to come and *help*.

The ground is *rocky* and the well is *far*. There is plenty of work for *everyone*.

So the dog dashed off into the desert. As he searched for the camel, he found another fine stick to add to the pile of firewood.

Finally, he found the camel beside a small oasis.

Wake up, O Camel!

DOINK

Stand up! Follow me back to our *fine* farm where you will fetch and carry like the *rest of us!*

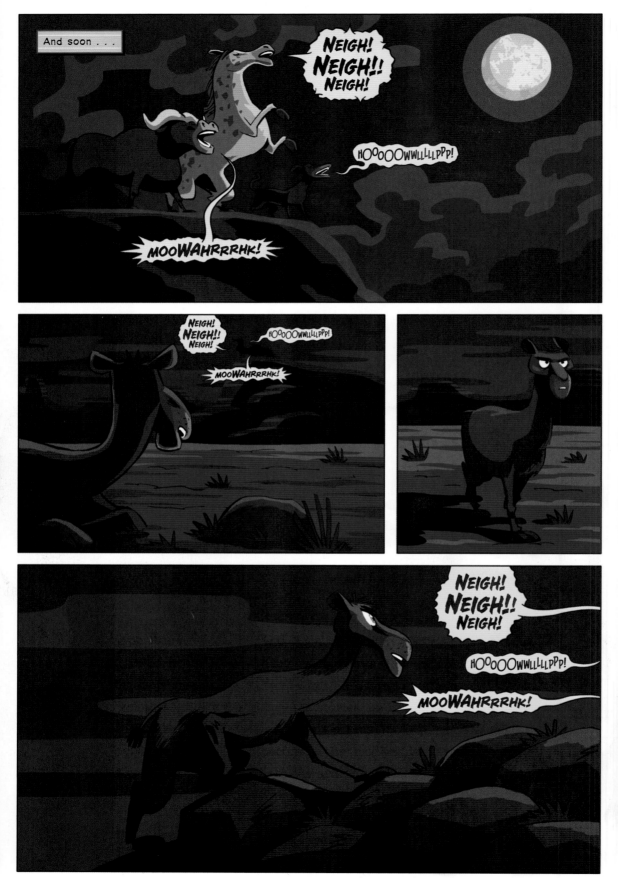

And the Camel humphed himself, humph and all, and ran to join Horse, Dog and Ox who were waiting for him at the top of the sand dune.

And he has never yet learned how to behave.

THE Camel's hump is an ugly lump
    Which well you may see at the Zoo;
But uglier yet is the hump we get
    From having too little to do.

Kiddies and grown-ups too-oo-oo,
If we haven't enough to do-oo-oo,
    We get the hump—
    Cameelious hump—
The hump that is black and blue!

We climb out of bed with a frouzly head
    And a snarly-yarly voice.
We shiver and scowl and we grunt and we growl
    At our bath and our boots and our toys;

And there ought to be a corner for me
(And I know there is one for you)
    When we get the hump—
    Cameelious hump—
The hump that is black and blue!

The cure for this ill is not to sit still,
    Or frowst with a book by the fire;
But to take a large hoe and a shovel also,
    And dig till you gently perspire;

And then you will find that the sun and the wind.
And the Djinn of the Garden too,
    Have lifted the hump—
    The horrible hump—
The hump that is black and blue!

I get it as well as you-oo-oo—
If I haven't enough to do-oo-oo—
    We all get hump—
    Cameelious hump—
Kiddies and grown-ups too! *

* Poem by Rudyard Kipling.

32

# CONCLUSION

## NEW SPECIMEN:
## SINGLE-HUMPED CAMEL

Camel urine is as thick as syrup, which is just plain gross. As the camel goes without water, the kidneys concentrate the urine, leading to its thickness.

When provoked, a camel will spit a foul-smelling, green fluid from its stomach all over you. At all costs, avoid provoking a camel.

Camels can kick in all four directions with all four legs. Must find a way to turn this skill into trained dancing.

SPEED LIMIT **65**

Camels can run up to 65 miles per hour, especially if it is to escape work.

FAT

A camel's hump stores fat. The size of the hump changes, depending on the amount of food the camel eats. When running low on food, the camel's body uses the fat stored in the hump, causing it to lean over and droop. How embarrassing!

SPEED LIMIT **65**

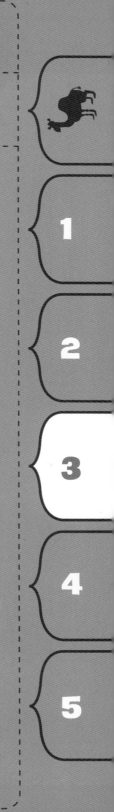

1

2

3

4

5

# LEARN MORE

Use this handy list of terms and questions to get you started on your own research of the magnificent camel!

## TERMS

| | |
|---|---|
| Arabia | (uh-RAY-bee-uh)—a peninsula in southwest Asia |
| bad-tempered | (BAD TEM-purd)—cross or cranky |
| Djinn | (JIN)—a mythical creature that has magical powers |
| idleness | (EYE-duhl-ness)—a state of being lazy and unwilling to do work |
| milkweed | (MILK-weed)—any of various herbs with milky juice and flowers usually in dense clusters |
| oasis | (oh-AY-siss)—a place in a desert where there is water and plants and trees grow |
| prickles | (PRIK-uhls)—small sharp points or a sharp pointed parts (like thorns on a plant) that stick out |
| tamarisks | (TAM-uh-risks)—any of a genus of chiefly desert shrubs of Eurasia and Africa that have small narrow leaves and clusters of tiny flowers |

# DISCUSSION

1  Why do you think the camel refused to do his share of the work?

2  Kipling says that Camel "has never learned to behave." How do you think he feels about the camel based on this line?

3  Kipling ended his field report with a poem, found on page 32. Discuss the poem. What tone does it have? Who is the speaker? Who is the audience?

# RESEARCH

1  Review Kipling's observation, and analyze the personalities of the animals. Write a paragraph comparing and contrasting them.

2  Research how camels use their humps. While the Djinn used the hump to punish Camel, did he actually help him in some ways? Explain your answer.

3  We now know how the camel got its hump. Write your own story about how the oxen got his horns, the horse got his mane, or dog got his tail.

## Rudyard Kipling

### RUDYARD KIPLING
### Founder/Guide

Joseph Rudyard Kipling was born in Bombay, India, on December 30, 1865. He is best known for his short story collections *The Jungle Book*, published in 1894, and *Just So Stories*, published in 1902. He wrote a variety of other short stories, including "Kim" and "The Man Who Would Be King," and many poems. In 1907, he received the Nobel Prize in Literature, becoming the first English-language writer and youngest person to win the award. On January 18, 1936, he died in London at age 70.

# LOUISE SIMONSON
## Retelling author

Louise Simonson writes about monsters, fantasy characters, and superheroes. She wrote the award-winning Power Pack series, several best-selling X-Men titles, Web of Spider-man for Marvel Comics, and Superman: Man of Steel and Steel for DC Comics. She is married to comic artist and writer Walter Simonson and lives in the suburbs of New York City.

# PEDRO RODRIGUEZ
## Illustrator

Pedro Rodriguez studied illustration at the Fine Arts School in Barcelona, Spain. He has worked in design, marketing, and advertising, creating books, logos, animated films, and music videos. Rodriguez lives in Barcelona with his wife, Gemma, and their daughter, Maya.

| JULIE GASSMAN | editor |
| DONALD LEMKE | managing editor |
| MICHAEL DAHL | editorial director |
| BOB LENTZ | designer & letterer |
| HEATHER KINDSETH | creative director |

1

2

3

4

5

# ALSO AVAILABLE FROM . . .

Published by Capstone Global Library Limited, a company incorporated in England and Wales having its registered office at 7 Pilgrim Street, London, EC4V 6LB - Registered company number: 6695582

Text © Raintree 2012    First published in India in 2012
The moral rights of the proprietor have been asserted.

ISBN 978-1-406-25359-7 (paperback)
16 15 14 13 12
10 9 8 7 6 5 4 3 2 1

A full catalogue record for this book is available from the British Library

Printed at Multivista Global Limited

www.raintreepublishers.co.uk
Email: myorders@raintreepublishers.co.uk

**Bloomington, Chicago, Mankato, Oxford**